Alan Ridout

PRELUDES, INTERLUDES
& POSTLUDES

FIFTEEN PIECES FOR ORGAN

First published in Great Britain by
KEVIN MAYHEW LTD
Rattlesden
Bury St Edmunds
Suffolk IP30 0SZ

ISBN 086209 149 7

Cover design by Juliette Clarke and Graham Johnstone
Music setting by Musicprint Ltd, London
Printed and bound in Great Britain by
J.B. Offset Printers (Marks Tey) Limited

Contents

Foreword

The fifteen pieces in Preludes, Interludes and Postludes have been written for meditative or celebratory moments during services but they may also be used in other ways: they are useful studies in a variety of playing techniques as well as teaching pieces.

For those organists on the look-out for new concert items the fifteen pieces may be played as Sonatinas by grouping Nos. 1, 2 and 3, Nos. 4, 5 and 6, Nos. 7, 8 and 9, Nos. 10, 11 and 12 and Nos. 13, 14 and 15.

About the Composer

Alan Ridout, born in 1934, is one of England's most prolific composers, producing a steady stream of works in most forms: symphonies, operas, ballet music, chamber music, song cycles and church music.

He studied with Jacob and Howells at the Royal College of Music, and later with Fricker, Tippett, and the Netherlands composer Henk Badings. He has taught at four universities, including Oxford and Cambridge, and for over twenty years was also a professor at the Royal College of Music.

To Don Kerr

1. Prelude

ALAN RIDOUT

2. Chant

ALAN RIDOUT

3. Toccatina

ALAN RIDOUT

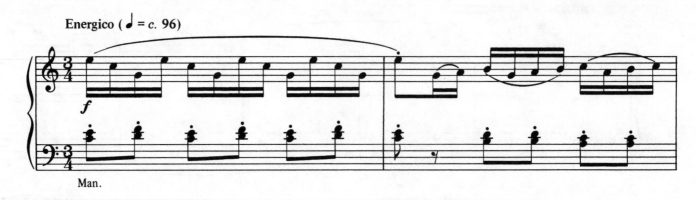

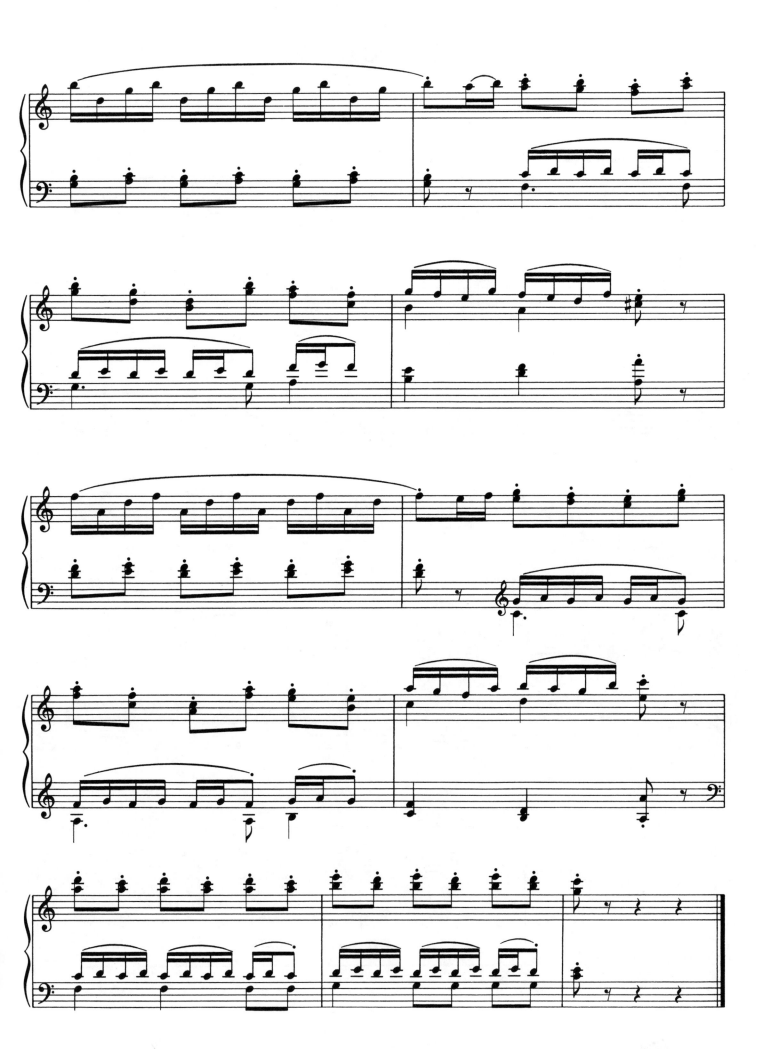

To Graham Knott

4. Invocation

ALAN RIDOUT

Ped.

Man.

9

5. Ground

ALAN RIDOUT

6. Air

ALAN RIDOUT

To Nancy Ludwig

7. Introit

ALAN RIDOUT

15

8. Meditation

ALAN RIDOUT

Adagio (♩ = c. 52)

9. Chorale

ALAN RIDOUT

To Stephen Crisp

10. Procession

ALAN RIDOUT

20

11. Song

ALAN RIDOUT

12. Elegy

ALAN RIDOUT

Lento (♩ = c. 42)

Man.

Ped.

To Robert Ludwig

13. Fanfare

ALAN RIDOUT

stacc.

Man.

Ped.

27

14. Soliloquy

ALAN RIDOUT

29

15. Finale

ALAN RIDOUT

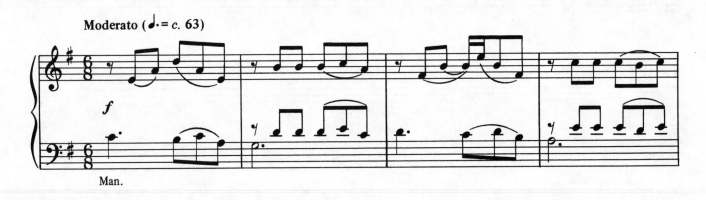

Fine Organ Music from Kevin Mayhew

QUIET-TIME MUSIC

15 Interludes for organ by COLIN MAWBY

Every service has times when quiet music is needed, especially for the Communion, and these fifteen superbly crafted Interludes in a variety of keys and time signatures are designed to fill those moments.

All the pieces are easily played and each carries the composer's distinctive voice and style.

Those familiar with Colin Mawby's work will be delighted by this addition to his lengthening list of compositions. Those who have not yet come across this outstanding composer should rectify the situation very quickly!

1405376

A YEAR OF PRAISE

25 Hymn Preludes by MALCOLM ARCHER

An invaluable collection for the organist who wishes to integrate his musical contribution with the hymns in the service. Malcolm Archer has taken twenty-five well known hymns and written a short, attractive prelude on each. Nothing here to trouble the technique but plenty to charm the ear.

There are hymn preludes on the following tunes:

Winchester New; Merton; Bristol; St. George; Cranham; Corde Natus; Humility; Stuttgart; Dix; Aus Der Tiefe (Heinlein); Caswall; St. Theodulph; Rockingham; Easter Hymn; St. Fulbert; St. Albinus; Llanfair; Veni, Creator Spiritus; Capetown; Laus Deo; St. Peter; Billing; Franconia; Dominus Regit Me; Monkland.

1425310

TWO HUNDRED LAST VERSES

Arranged by NOEL RAWSTHORNE

There are few musical pleasures more spine-tingling than a really good organ arrangement of the last verse of a hymn. Noel Rawsthorne is a past-master at providing a touch of spice to the harmonies of an unsuspecting hymn-tune, but one who knows what is possible on the average parish church organ. In *Two Hundred Last Verses* you will find colourful, manageable arrangements requiring only moderate technique.

Under one cover *Two Hundred Last Verses* provides the organist with all the hymns he is ever likely to need – and fabulous value, as usual, at only 5 pence a hymn!

1405527

Please send for our Catalogue of the best Organ and Church Music

MUSIC FOR THE BRIDE

32 Popular wedding pieces arranged by NOEL RAWSTHORNE

Music for the Bride is a collection of the most popular music requested for weddings, all arranged so that it falls comfortably under the hands (and feet) of the organist who has a reasonable technique.

Organists are renowned for losing their individual music sheets so *Music for the Bride*, all under one cover, will be a boon.

In addition to the music book, Noel Rawsthorne has recorded 20 pieces – ideal as an aid to help couples choose their wedding music in the comfort of their own home.

Bridal March from 'Lohengrin'	R. Wagner
Fanfare for a Bride	Noel Rawsthorne
Trumpet Voluntary	J. Clarke
Two Trumpet Tunes and Air	H. Purcell
Te Deum Prelude	M. A. Charpentier
March from 'Occasional Oratorio'	G. F. Handel
March from 'Scipio'	G. F. Handel
Arrival of the Queen of Sheba	G. F. Handel
Gavotte	W. Boyce
St. Anthony Chorale	Attr to F. J. Haydn
Ave Maria	F. Schubert
Air from 'Water Music'	G. F. Handel
Interlude I	Noel Rawsthorne
Coro from 'Water Music'	G. F. Handel
Finale from 'Fireworks Music'	G. F. Handel
Ballet des Matelotz	M. Praetorius
Interlude II	Noel Rawsthorne
Largo from 'Serse'	G. F. Handel
Andante Tranquillo from 'Capriol Suite'	Peter Warlock
Siciliana from Concerto No. 5	G. F. Handel
Bourrée from 'Water Music'	G. F. Handel
Prière	Noel Rawsthorne
Prelude on the Londonderry Air	Noel Rawsthorne
Minuet from Concerto No. 9	G. F. Handel
Two Versets on 'Love Divine'	Noel Rawsthorne
Andante	J. H. Fiocco
Jesu, Joy of Man's Desiring	J. S. Bach
Toccata in D Minor	J. S. Bach
Sheep May Safely Graze	J. S. Bach
Gavotte from 5th French Suite	J. S. Bach
Air from Suite No. 3 in D	J. S. Bach
Wedding March	F. Mendelssohn

1405375 Music Book
1405373 Cassette

Kevin Mayhew Ltd
Rattlesden   Bury St Edmunds
Suffolk IP30 0SZ

Phone 0449 737978   Fax 0449 737834